ART ROM

I ♥ Fairies

Created by the Top That! team

TOP THAT!™

Published by Top That! Publishing
Tide Mill Way, Woodbridge, Suffolk, IP12 1AP
www.topthatpublishing.com
Copyright © 2003 Top That! Publishing plc
Top That! is a Registered Trademark of Top That! Publishing plc

I Love Fairies

If you're a real fairy lover, then you'll love this superb book and CD-ROM full of fun, easy-to-make projects. The CD is packed with great fairy images and the book explains exactly how to use them, in simple step-by-step instructions. Learn all about fairies and their behaviour, how they communicate, where they live and much more!

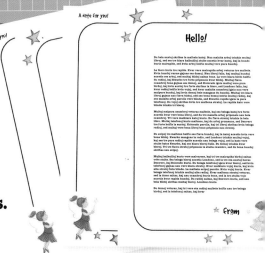

Themed Projects

There are several themed projects in the book. You can make your own personalised stationery, including notepaper, envelopes, labels and postcards.

Party Ideas

Discover how to make a great hanging picture mobile. Use the brilliant party ideas with nameplaces, invitations, party hats and blowers.

Hold a Party

Why not hold a fairy party for all your friends? You will also learn how to transform objects with découpage, from a decorated box to a mirror.

Projects to Make

You can also print the images from the CD onto acetate, which will help you to make a beautiful light catcher. You can turn your bedroom into a fairy's playground by decorating boxes, mirrors and 'do not disturb' signs.

Find Out More

As if that's not enough, there's also information about how you can find out more about fairies and the environments in which they live, and where you might find them.

We've even found some websites for you! So what are you waiting for?

Start making some projects!

I Love Fairies

Fairies are enchanting creatures who live in a magical world full of elves, pixies and talking flowers. If you believe in fairies, then listen carefully as every flower will tell you a story and every tree will be your lifelong friend. Hiding at the bottom of your garden, or under a tree, all you have to do to see a fairy is believe.

Best Places to see Fairies
- At a crossroads.
- By a lake or a stream.
- In the woods.
- By fences or hedgerows.

Best Times to see Fairies
- At sunrise.
- At sunset.
- When it is misty.
- On the night of a full moon.
- On the night of a new moon.

4

I Love Fairies

How do you know if the fairies are near?

1. If you find a fairy ring in your garden you know the fairies aren't far away.

2. If you hear music and singing, but cannot see where it is coming from, it will be fairies playing.

3. If you have lots of flowers and trees in your garden, you can be sure that the fairies will be near.

4. If you hear the wind whispering, it is the fairies talking to each other.

5. If you see stars at night, the fairies will be out.

6. If you have sweet dreams, the fairies have watched over you in bed.

7. If you hear leaves rustle, or see the grass blades sway, the fairies are dancing.

8. If the tooth fairy visits you whilst you are asleep, you know she's watching over you always.

Fairies come in all shapes and sizes... read on to find out more about some famous fairies!

The Tooth Fairy

She is the most magical of the fairies, a tiny creature who visits boys and girls all over the world. If you put a tooth under your pillow at night, she'll leave behind one of her sparkling coins. She'll only take really clean teeth, so make sure you look after yours!

The Sugar Plum Fairy

A little girl called Clara travelled to the magical Land of Sweets as a reward for her bravery. She was taken to the palace of the Sugar Plum Fairy who commanded a royal festival for her to watch, including a beautiful dance by Sugar Plum herself.

Cinderella's Fairy Godmother

Wouldn't you love to have a godmother who transformed your rags to beautiful clothes, put you into a golden carriage and sent you to a ball? That's what happened to lucky Cinderella, who met the prince of her dreams with the help of this very special fairy.

Tinkerbell

This lively fairy appeared in a little girl's bedroom in search of Peter Pan's shadow. After stitching it back on, she sprinkled her special fairy dust on humans to help them fly to Never Never Land in search of adventure.

Titania

The Queen of the Fairies, this beautiful lady rests in a floral hideaway under a river bank where a host of fairies sing her to sleep with their peaceful lullaby. Their singing protects her from snakes, snails and any evil spirits.

User Guide to CD-ROM

FOR PC USERS

The program should run automatically. If not, double click on the 'my computer' icon on the desktop, and then on the 'CD drive' icon. Then double click the title 'art-pc.exe'.

FOR MACINTOSH USERS

Double click on the 'CD' icon on the desktop and then double click the title 'art-mac'.

MINIMUM SYSTEM REQUIREMENTS

Screen resolution: 800 x 600, colour depth: 32 bit (true colour), CD ROM facility.

• **PC USERS** – Intel Pentium® 166 processor running Windows™ 95/98 or NT version 4.0 or later, 32 MB of installed RAM, and a colour monitor.

• **MACINTOSH USERS** – Power PC 120 Macintosh® running system 8.1 or later, 32 MB of installed RAM and a colour monitor.

NOTE: When you start up the CD, choose your preferred language to read it in, by clicking on the flag.

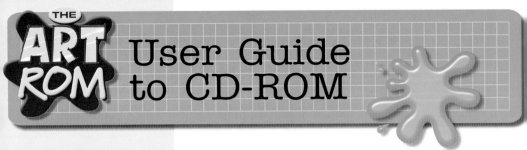

CD TIPS

To help you understand your CD-ROM, follow the steps below to design your own fairy letterhead.

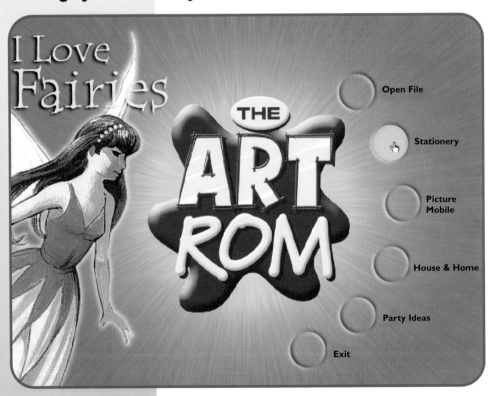

1 Choose the 'Stationery' section from the main menu.

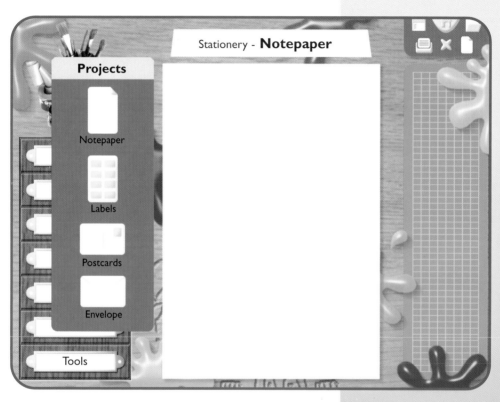

Stationery - **Notepaper**

Projects

Notepaper

Labels

Postcards

Envelope

Tools

2 Click on the 'Projects' drawer and choose 'Notepaper'. You will find that you have to close one drawer, by clicking on it, before you can open the next.

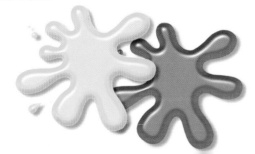

User Guide to CD-ROM

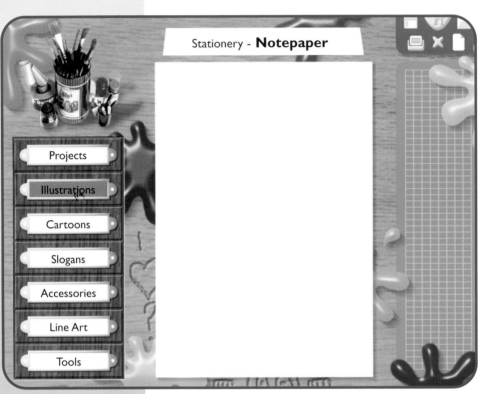

Stationery - **Notepaper**

Projects

Illustrations

Cartoons

Slogans

Accessories

Line Art

Tools

3 Next, add a picture. You can choose from illustrations, cartoons or line art pictures. To choose a picture, simply click on either the 'Illustrations', 'Line Art' or 'Cartoons' drawer. Don't forget to close the drawer when you've finished with what's inside.

User Guide to CD-ROM

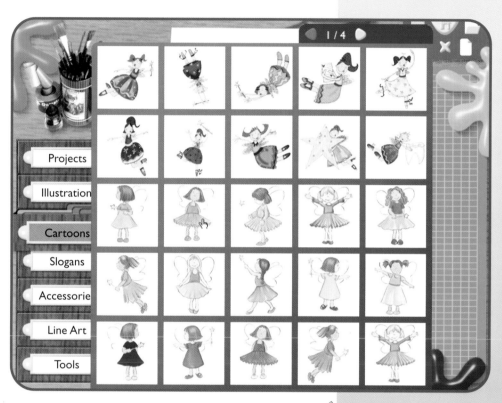

Projects

Illustration

Cartoons

Slogans

Accessorie

Line Art

Tools

4 You will notice that the pictures are in a grid. At the top of the screen there are left and right arrows and numbers to indicate how many pages of pictures there are and the page you are on. Use the arrows to move from one page of pictures to the next, until you find an image you want to use.

User Guide to CD-ROM

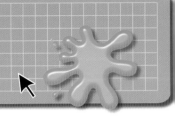

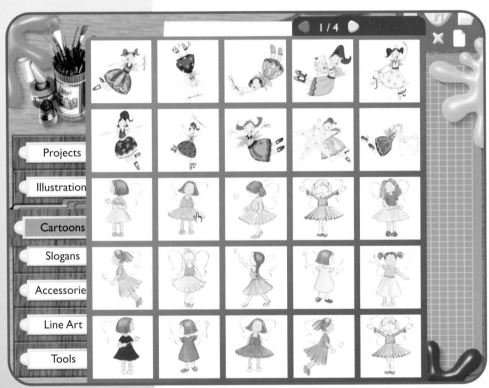

Projects

Illustration

Cartoons

Slogans

Accessorie

Line Art

Tools

5 To make your choice, click on the image. You'll notice that it appears on the green pasteboard to the right. You can have up to eight images at a time on the pasteboard. Remember to close the drawer when you have finished what you are doing.

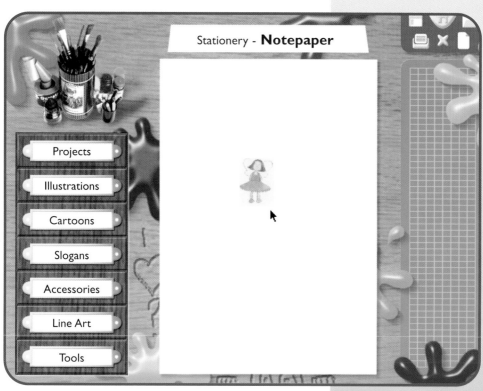

6 Drag the picture onto the page. Do this by clicking on the image that you want to select, which will turn yellow. This means the picture is highlighted and can now be altered. Still holding the mouse button, move the image onto your chosen position on the page.

User Guide to CD-ROM

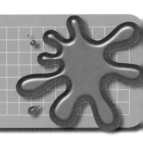

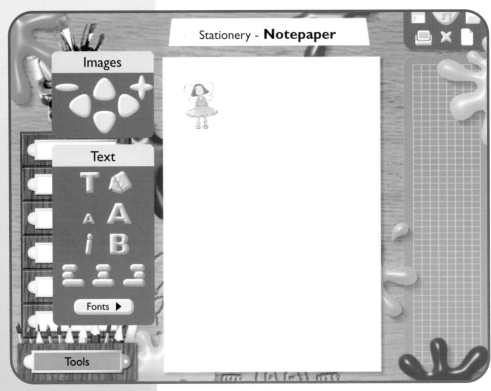

Stationery - **Notepaper**

Images

Text

T

A A

i B

Fonts ▶

Tools

7 To flip the picture the other way round, click on the 'Tools' drawer. Then click on the left/right arrows to flip it left or right, or the up/down arrows to flip it upside down. You'll notice that there are + and − buttons which you can use to make the picture larger or smaller if you want to.

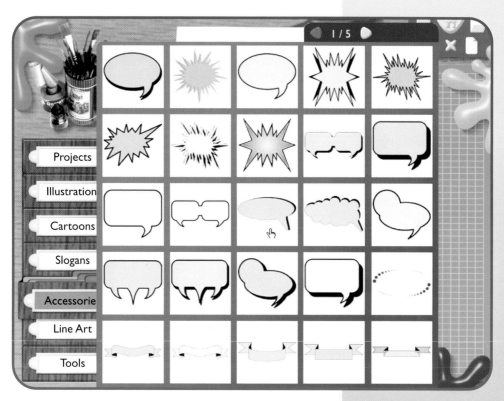

8 You may want to add accessories to the picture. Use the 'Accessories' drawer to add items to the picture such as flowers, stars and even fairy cakes! To add speech bubbles to the picture, click on the 'Accessories' drawer, then choose the image that you want and click on it.

15

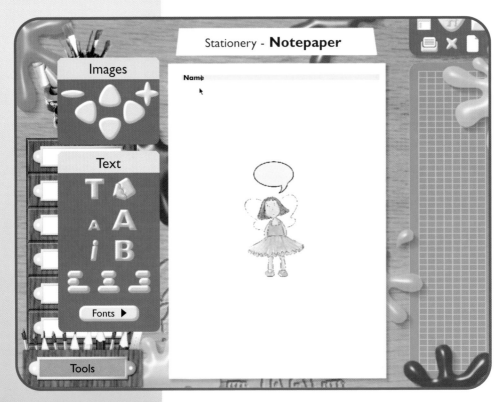

9 Now you need to add your name and address. Open the 'Tools' drawer, then click on the big 'T' and you should notice a yellow bar appear on the page. This is where you do your typing. Type in your name and address, then click anywhere on the page to enter the text. To move the text around click on it, then drag it to where you want it on the page. Any time you want to enter text or a picture, simply click elsewhere on the page. The yellow highlight will then disappear. You can have five text boxes at a time on a page. If you try to put more on an alert box will appear, as will always happen if you do something you shouldn't.

User Guide to CD-ROM

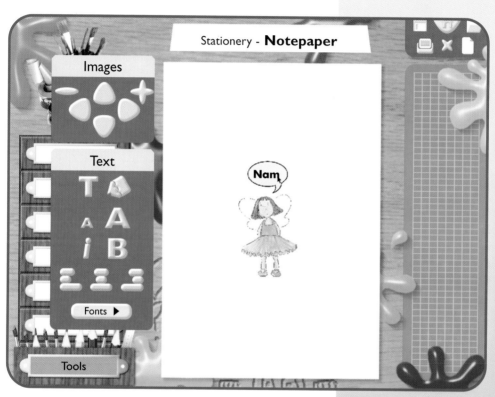

Stationery - **Notepaper**

Images

Text

Fonts ▶

Tools

Nam

10 To alter the size and style of the text, you need to highlight the area of text you want to change by clicking on it. To make text larger, click on the big 'A' button and to make it smaller, click on the small 'A' button. To make it bold, click on the big 'B' button, and to italicise the text, click on the 'i' button. To align the text to either the left, right or centre, click the icons (see page 19).

User Guide to CD-ROM

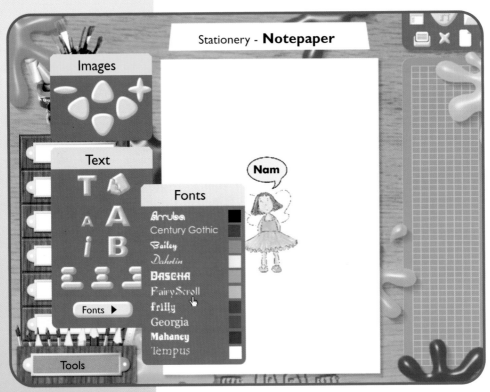

11 To change the font, make sure the text is still highlighted and move the mouse cursor over the 'fonts' button. A drop-down menu will appear. Click on the name of the font that you like, and any of the coloured squares next to the fonts to change the colour. Print the finished project when you are happy with it, by clicking on the 'print' icon.

User Guide to CD-ROM

ICONS EXPLAINED

Click on the 'home' icon to get back to the main menu.

Click on the 'cross' icon to delete a single picture. Just highlight a picture, then click on the 'X' to delete it.

Click on the 'page' icon to delete the whole page. You will not be able to start a different project until you have deleted any images still on the pasteboard.

Click on the 'print' icon to print your work at any stage.

These icons are the 'align' icons. This icon will align text to the left when you click on it.

This icon will centre align text when you click on it.

This icon will right align text when you click on it.

The pencil icon allows you to edit the text. Highlight the text first then click on the pencil icon.

Save your work at any time by clicking on the 'save' icon in the top right-hand corner. Give your file a name when you save it and choose a place to save it, such as the desktop. To re-save it, click on the 'save' icon. You will have to re-type the file name in order to save it again. An alert box will pop up, asking you whether you want to replace the original or not. Click 'yes' if you have a PC, and 'replace' if you're using a Mac.

Open a file by clicking on the 'open' icon.

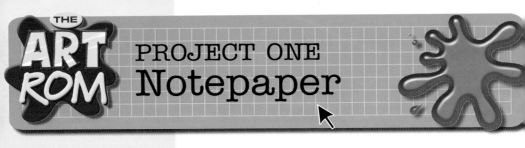

PROJECT ONE
Notepaper

Design your own fantastic fairy stationery – from notepaper to postcards.

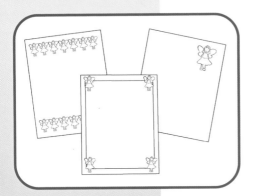

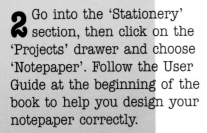

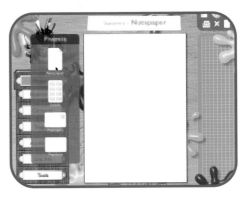

1 First, decide how you want your designs to look. You could use a border across the top and bottom of the paper, a border around the whole page or a simple letterhead design.

2 Go into the 'Stationery' section, then click on the 'Projects' drawer and choose 'Notepaper'. Follow the User Guide at the beginning of the book to help you design your notepaper correctly.

3 When you are happy with the designs, print them out to see what they look like. If you like what you have created, print out several copies of each design. You could also draw a box to write in.

PROJECT TWO
Envelopes

You will need:
- scissors
- a glue stick

2 Choose the required images and position them on the top half of the template. You can move the images around until you find the best position.

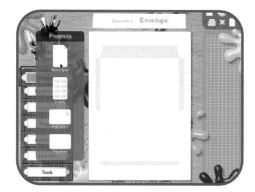

1 In the 'Stationery' section, click on the 'Projects' drawer and choose 'Envelope'. An envelope template will appear.

3 Now, print the envelope template and carefully cut it out. Glue the grey parts together to make the envelope. Your envelope is now ready, so get writing!

21

THE ART ROM

PROJECT THREE
Labels

You will need:
- A4 sheet of eight white sticky labels

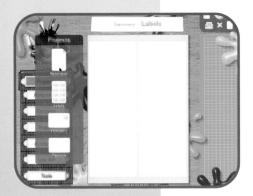

1 In the 'Stationery' section, click on the 'Projects' drawer and choose 'Labels'. A template will appear, with eight labels.

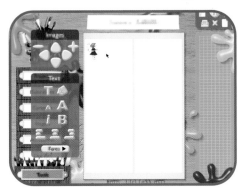

2 Choose an image and drag it into place on the template. You can add text if you want to, such as 'To' and 'From'.

3 Print onto the sheet of labels. You will be able to buy these from any computer or stationery shop. Attach to a gift or parcel, and neatly write who it is for, and from, on the label.

You will need:
- thin card
- scissors

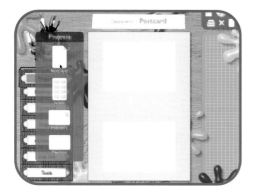

1 In the 'Stationery' section, click on the 'Projects' drawer and choose 'Postcard'. Two postcard templates will appear.

2 Click on your chosen images, and drag them into position on both the templates.

3 Print the postcards onto thin card, cut them out and they are ready to send to all your favourite friends!

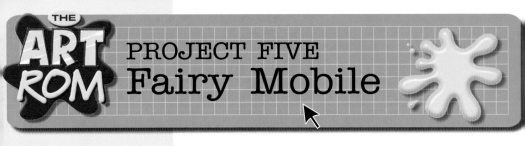

Make a picture mobile of several playful fairies flying and dancing around your room!

You will need:
- card
- scissors
- a glue stick
- a reel of cotton
- a marker pen
- a side plate
- a needle
- sequins

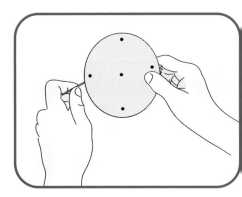

2 Make five marks, as shown, on one side of the circle. Ask an adult to pierce each of these points with a needle.

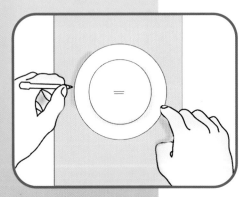

1 Draw around a side plate onto a sheet of coloured card – the diameter should be approximately 20 cm. Ask an adult to cut the circle out.

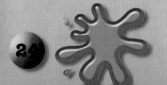

24

PROJECT FIVE
Fairy Mobile

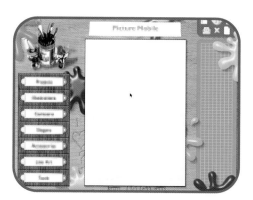

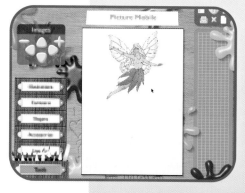

3 Select 'Picture Mobile' from the main menu. A blank page will appear, with a grey section on the bottom half. Choose some images and drag them onto the top half of the page. You can have up to four at a time, but one large one at a time might be best.

4 You may wish to alter the size, so that they are large enough for the mobile. Use the + and – buttons to increase and decrease the size. Click on the 'print' icon and the image will automatically face the other way. This page will be the preview. If you are not happy with the image, click on the 'back' button, change the image and click 'print' again to view the page.

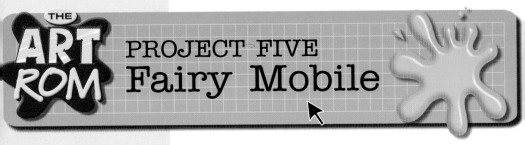

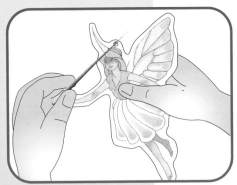

5 Print the page and fold it exactly in half. Stick the pages together, then cut the image out. Ask an adult to pierce holes in the top of the image with a needle.

6 Use a piece of string to measure the outside of the circle. Cut a long piece of card, slightly longer than this length, to go around the circle. The width of the card can be as narrow as you like. You will need to add an extra centimetre along one edge for the tabs to attach it to the circle. You can decorate each mobile holder differently – use your imagination.

7 Tie a piece of cotton through the top of each image, then tie each piece of cotton at different heights through the holes in the circle of card. Attach a sequin to the end of each length of cotton to stop it from falling through the hole.

8 To hang the mobile up, ask an adult to make three evenly-spaced holes around the edge of the cardboard band with a needle. Thread three even lengths of cotton through these holes, securing on the inside with a sequin. Tie the cotton lengths together, from the outside, in the middle and hang the mobile up. Do not tie them from the inside, as the mobile will then tilt and not hang properly.

PROJECT FIVE
Fairy Mobile

PROJECT SIX
Nameplaces

Fairies are very sociable. They'd probably love the chance to have a fairy party! You can make nameplaces, hats and party invitations – all with lively fairies dancing around on them.

You will need:
- thin card
- scissors

2 Print out the template onto thin card. Carefully cut the page into four.

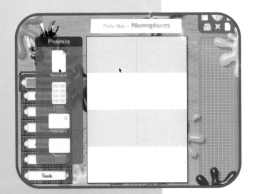

1 Go into the 'Party Ideas' section of the main menu. Click on the 'Projects' drawer and select 'Nameplaces'. A template will appear. Select some images and drag them onto the white parts of the template. Add the person's name next to the picture.

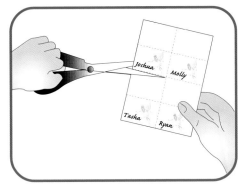

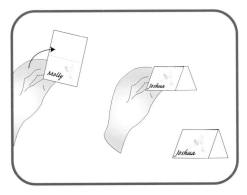

3 Fold each nameplace in half along the dotted line.

PROJECT SEVEN
Party Invitations

You will need:
- paper

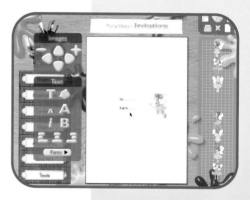

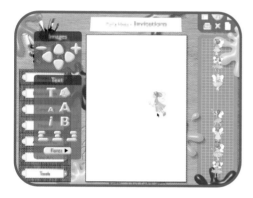

1 Select 'Invitations' from the 'Projects' drawer in the 'Party Ideas' section of the main menu. Select your images and drag them onto the paper.

2 Type in text such as 'To', 'From', and 'You are invited to a party at...' and the rest of the details. Then print onto coloured paper and fill in the rest of the details in your best handwriting.

You are invited
to a party
at

THE ART ROM

PROJECT EIGHT
Fairy Blowers

You will need:
- party blowers
- scissors
- a glue stick
- glitter

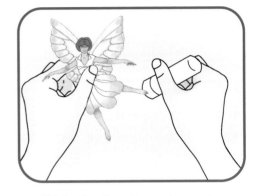

2 Stick the images onto party blowers. Add glitter if you want to make them more sparkly.

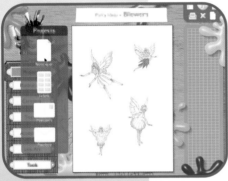

1 Select 'Blowers' from the 'Projects' drawer in the 'Party Ideas' section of the main menu. Select some images and drag them onto the page. They will need to be quite small to fit on the blowers. Print and cut them out.

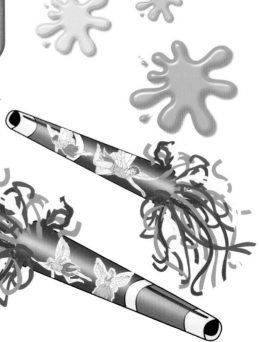

You will need:
- party hats
- scissors
- a glue stick
- coloured pens

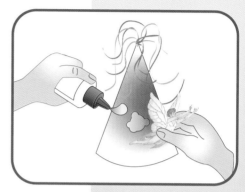

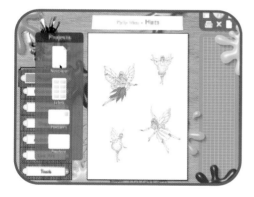

2 Glue them onto party hats. To jazz them up, add glitter or some patterns with coloured pens.

1 Select 'Party Hats' from the 'Projects' drawer in the 'Party Ideas' section of the main menu. Select the images you want and print and cut them out.

Design your own fairy boxes and pots, using découpage. You may need an adult to help you. Don't forget, when gluing, painting or varnishing, always make sure you do it in a well-ventilated area. It may get messy so wear old clothes and put lots of newspaper down first.

You will need:
- a gift box
- paint
- scissors
- a glue stick
- a paintbrush

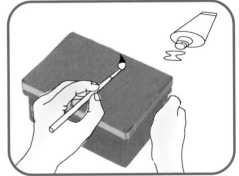

2 If you want to change the colour of your gift box, carefully paint it and leave to dry. Alternatively, you could cover it with wrapping paper.

1 Go into the 'House and Home' drawer on the main menu, and select 'Découpage'. Select one or two images from the CD and print them out. Carefully cut them out.

3 Cut around the images, leaving a tab of approximately 1 cm along the bottom. Fold the tab, glue along it and attach to the top of the box.

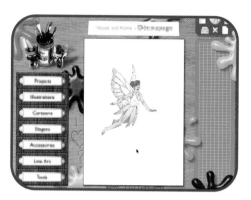

You will need:
- card
- sticky-back clear plastic film
- scissors
- glue stick

1 Select 'Découpage' from the 'Projects' drawer in the 'House and Home' section. Choose your favourite image and print it out.

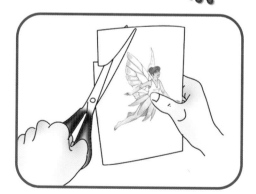

2 Cut a semi-circle over the top of the image, and two sloping sides below it (see Step 3). Then cut a 20 cm x 7 cm rectangle from the coloured card.

3 Glue your image onto the top of the rectangle. When it is dry, cover both sides of the bookmark with clear sticky film. Cut two slits, 1 cm from the edge of the sloping sides and long enough to meet in the middle. This tab will hold the book's pages.

PROJECT TWELVE
Mirror

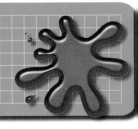

You will need:

- scissors
- a wide-framed mirror
- PVA glue
- a brush
- a glue stick
- sticky putty

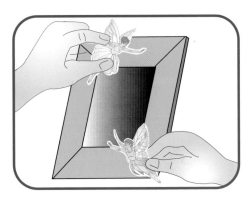

2 Arrange the pictures around the frame, and stick them on with the sticky putty. Try them out randomly or in a pattern.

3 When you're happy with the positioning, stick the images onto the frame with a glue stick. How about sticking on some embroidered flowers or glittery gems for an extra-special effect?

1 Select 'Découpage' from the 'Projects' drawer in the 'House and Home' section. Select your favourite images and drag them onto the page. Print and cut them out.

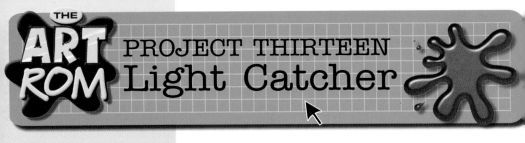

All you need is some acetate sheets, which you can get from any stationery or computer shop, and this CD, to make a stunning light catcher.

You will need:
- acetate sheet
- scissors
- ribbon
- a needle
- paper stars

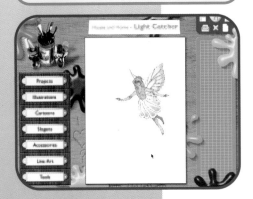

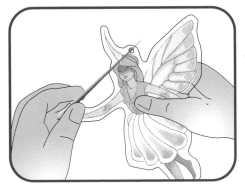

1 Go into the 'House and Home' section of the main menu. Click on the 'Projects' drawer and select 'Light catcher'. Choose an image and drag it onto the page. Make it fairly big, using the 'Tools' drawer. Print it onto a sheet of acetate and cut it out, leaving a 2.5 cm border around the edge.

2 Ask an adult to make a small hole with a needle in the top of each of the cut-outs, then cut some ribbon and tie it into a bow. Stitch it to hold it together. Cut another length of ribbon, tie in a loop and stitch to the bow. Thread the ribbon through the cut-out. Hang it up near a window, to make a brilliant light catcher.

3 Alternatively, you could print out a really big image onto acetate. Cut around it in a rectangular shape and attach cardboard panels to make a frame. Stick on some silver stars, and your light catcher is ready to hang up!

You will need:
- coloured or plain card
- scissors

1 Select 'Labels' from the 'Projects' drawer in the 'Stationery' section of the main menu. Drag one or two images onto the label template. You may have to make them quite small to fit.

2 Add text, saying 'To' and 'From'.

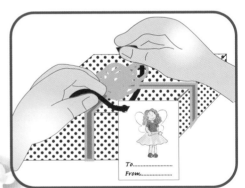

To.....................
From.....................

3 Print the tag onto card, cut out and attach to the present that you are going to give.

PROJECT FIFTEEN
Wrapping Paper

You will need:
- paper

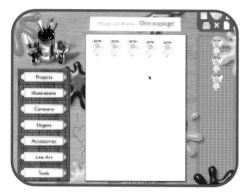

1 Select 'Découpage' from the 'Projects' drawer in the 'House and Home' section of the main menu. Choose some images and position them on the page. You might decide to have one image repeated, or several images.

2 Add text if you want, such as 'Happy Birthday' or 'Have a Great Day!' Why not try repeating the name of the person you are giving it to, in different fonts and sizes?

3 Print as many sheets as you need to wrap your presents in.

PROJECT SIXTEEN
Letter Box

You will need:
- a letter rack
- PVA glue
- a brush
- a glue stick
- scissors
- sticky putty

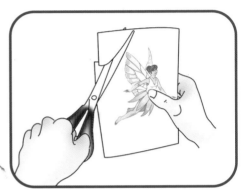

2 Print them out at the size you require. Now carefully cut them out.

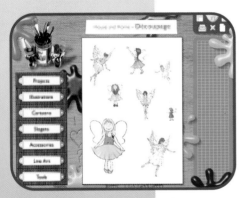

1 Select 'Découpage' from the 'Projects' drawer in the 'House and Home' section of the main menu. Select a few images and drag them onto the screen.

3 You will need to buy a letter rack, or revamp one you already have. Stick the images onto the rack. When you are happy with your design, varnish them with diluted PVA.

PROJECT SEVENTEEN
Greetings Card

You will need:
- coloured card
- coloured or plain paper
- string
- glue

2 Add text, if you want to, and cut it out. Fold a piece of card in half, cut a square window from the front, and hang your image from the top panel with string. Stick your message inside!

1 Select 'Découpage' from the 'Projects' drawer in the 'House and Home' section of the main menu. Choose an image and print it out.

PROJECT EIGHTTEEN
Jewellery Box

You will need:
- a clean box
- scissors
- PVA glue
- a brush
- a glue stick
- acetate sheets

1 Go into the 'House and Home' section of the main menu. Click on the 'Projects' drawer and select 'Découpage'. Select several images and drag them onto the page.

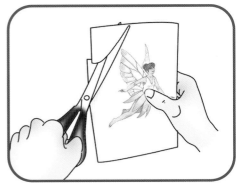

2 Print the images onto acetate and carefully cut them out. Position them on the surfaces of the box at various angles, until you're happy with the effect. Stick the pictures on with the glue stick, making sure to smooth all the edges down. Leave to dry.

3 Dilute some PVA with water, and then varnish the box completely. You may need to get an adult to help you with this. Leave to dry, then recoat at least twice. This will give it a waterproof, shiny effect.

You will need:
- coloured card
- scissors
- a glue stick
- a marker pen/
  coloured pens

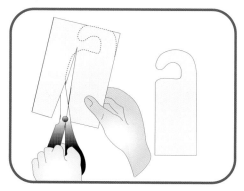

2 Go into the 'House and Home' section of the main menu, click on the 'Projects' drawer and select 'Découpage'. Drag and drop two images onto the screen, print them, and cut them out. Stick them to either side of the sign. Use a marker pen to write on messages like those shown on the hangers below.

1 Cut out the card in the shape of a sign. It can be in the shape of a fairy, or just a square, but it must have a hook so that you can hang it over your door handle.

FIND OUT MORE
About Fairies

FIND OUT MORE

There are lots of ways you can find out about fairies. Look in libraries and bookshops for picture and story books, or search the world wide web... here are some references to get you started!

Cicely Mary Barker drew beautiful pictures of fairies dressed in flower petals and leaves. To find out which fairy she drew for your favourite plant, go to **www.flowerfairies.com**

If you want to make a pretty fairy costume for a party, see **www.kidsdomain.com/craft/ _hcostume.html** to find out how!

For a beautiful bedtime story, perform a search under the word 'Cinderella'.

Or go to **www.kidsdomain.com/ holiday/xmas/music1/nutcracker. html** to read the magical story of 'The Nutcracker'.

Pictorial Index

This pictorial index contains all the images on the CD. You can use it to quickly find which picture you're looking for, without having to go through the CD.

Illustrations   Cartoons   Slogans   Accessories   Line Art

THE ART ROM Pictorial Index

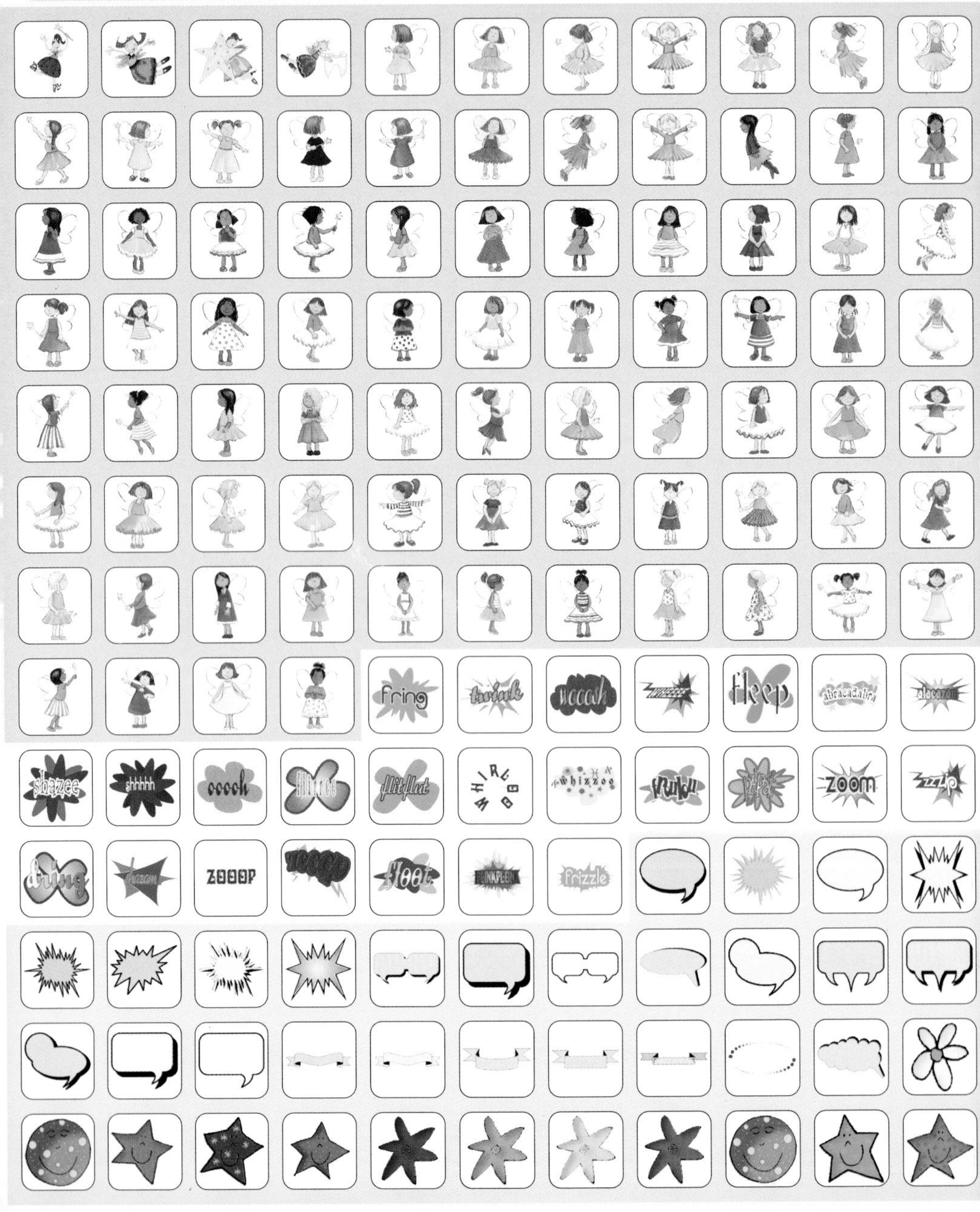

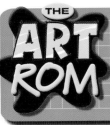

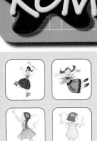

Pictorial Index

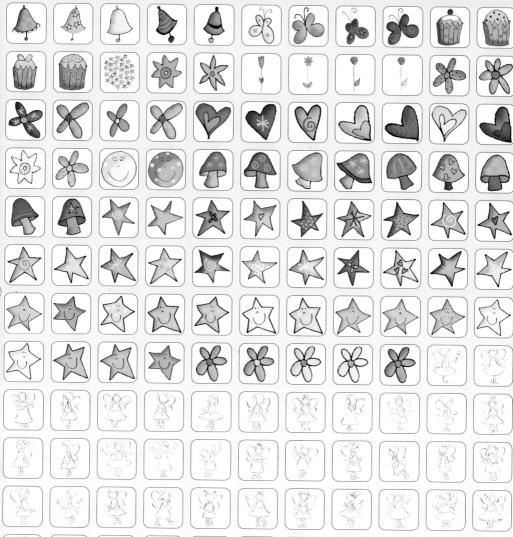

Pictorial Index

As well as these images, there are accessories and slogans which are universal throughout the I Love CD-ROM series.